THE POETRY OF MR MINEVAR

THE POETRY OF

MR MINEVAR

TONY RUSSELL

Matador
9 Priory Business Park,
Wistow Road, Kibworth Beauchamp,
Leicestershire. LE8 0RX
Tel: 0116 279 2299
Email: books@troubador.co.uk
Web: www.troubador.co.uk/matador
Twitter: @matadorbooks

ISBN 978 1800465 282

British Library Cataloguing in Publication Data.
A catalogue record for this book is available from the British Library.

Printed and bound in Great Britain by 4edge Limited
Typeset in 11pt Minion Pro by Troubador Publishing Ltd, Leicester, UK

Matador is an imprint of Troubador Publishing Ltd

To my family
Mum, Dad*, Greg, Will & Imo
*1927–2018

The hours of folly are measured by the clock; but of wisdom, no clock can measure.

William Blake

CONTENTS

PROLOGUE

'These are dark times,' said Mr Minevar.

'Yes, indeed they are.'

'Now lad, we've been chatting for a quarter of an hour or so, but what is it you want from me?'

'Well, the point is, Mr Minevar...'

'Call me George.'

'Well George, I work for the "Evening Echo" and we want to take soundings, if you pardon the pun, on your Artistic Life. I understand you wrote Poetry.'

'I dabbled.'

'I understand Mr Minevar, I mean George, that you dabbled quite a lot.'

'I double-dabbled.'

I looked at Mr Minevar, tweed of jacket, corduroy of trousers, red of nose, blue eyes. A treasure trove of stories, according to the locals of "The George and Dragon". To them, he was GEM; George Edward Minevar. And here we were, sitting outside the pub in the warm summer sunshine, I with my notebook and he, smoking his pipe, looking for all the world like Tolkien.

'The notion of Fashion,' pronounced Mr Minevar, 'is poppycock for peacocks.'

It was one of many quotations.

'What's on the Poetic Menu then George?'

'Many things: Darwin, Churchill, My Children, A Painting, Alcohol, Earthworms, Edward Lear, Love and Divorce, Marriage, and of course, Ovid.'

'An eclectic mix.'

'Yes, eclectic.'

'Where shall we start?'

'First,' said Mr Minevar, 'I have something to say,' and he put his hands together as if in prayer.

> 'Poetry aims at Truth
> I'm paraphrasing Plato.
> Be virtuous in what you write and do
> Just like the stoic Cato.'

'*Now* we can start.'

'I have in mind to begin with Ovid and Shakespeare. Next my children, Will and Imo. Then Earthworms, followed by Darwin. Those two are linked you know. Perhaps touch on Churchill and Alcohol. There's a wee dram of connection there as well. I'll then throw in the painting, but from thereon in, it is all downhill laddie. Edward Lear, Love and Divorce, Marriage. All downhill.'

Mr Minevar sighed as if he were flyfishing a painful memory.

OVID & SHAKESPEARE

'Well Mr Minevar, let's open with Ovid. I know a little about him, but only a smidge.'

'Sit back and learn laddie. Sit back and learn.'

But before Mr Minevar could start, I released my smidge.

'Mr Minevar, I believe Ovid was a maverick, disliked by the Emperor Augustus and sent into exile.'

'Indeed, that is so.'

'And Tiberius, after Augustus had died, wouldn't take him back.'

'Indeed, that is so.'

'That's *all* I know Mr Minevar.'

'I'm sure it is,' said Mr Minevar and immediately he slipped his voice into first gear:

'Ovid was a major poet
Who certainly was *not* a novice
Living within that golden age
Of Virgil, Livy... Horace.'

1

'Ovid was very clever laddie. And he knew it. And that ruffled a few feathers, not least that canny bird Augustus.'

Without warning, Mr Minevar burst into verse again.

'When there are days of fear and dread
May I suggest Ovid be read.
Catharsis cures our own neuroses
Try ingesting *Metamorphoses*

From creation onwards we are told
Of how humanity will unfold
Involving rape and much destruction
Like Semele's Zeus – induced combustion.

Sexual desire both good and evil
Are here most graphically described.
Tereus seduces his wife's sister
Eurydice's hand is Orpheus denied.'

'How sad, Mr Minevar, I mean, George. How very sad.'
'It gets worse:

Vain Narcissus dies from grieving
Pentheus killed by mum and aunt
Arachne and Minerva duel by weaving
Arachne can, Minerva can't.'

'And was Ovid influential, George?'
'Oh yes, one only has to read Shakespeare.'
And the poet-juggernaut juggered on:

'The English Bard owes much to Ovid.
Myths abound within his plays,
Embuing them with erudition;
'Tis aimed of course to court our praise.'

I interjected before Mr Minevar could get into his stride again.

'Mr Minevar, I mean George, was it not Ben Jonson who said of Shakespeare, "He was not of an age, but for all time"?'

'Indeed it was.'

'And was it not Hazlitt who raved, "If we wish to know the force of human genius, we should read Shakespeare"?'

'Indeed it was.'

'And was it not Dryden who, star-struck, said "'Shakespeare's magic could not copied be, within that circle none durst walk but he"?'

'Indeed it was. Just so. Now, may *I* continue with *my* own damp verse concerning the Myths and the Bard?:

They feature in *Titus Andronicus*
The Winter's Tale; *The Tempest* too
Love Labour's Lost and of course *Hamlet*
Romeo and Juliet to name but few

Allusions to myths pervade his verse
Illuminating how we feel
So skilful in his chosen task
So lacking an Achille's heel.'

'Bravo Mr Minevar! Bravo! But return to Ovid, I beg you.' Mr Minevar obliged, though in truth I could discern a slight grinding of the back molars.

'So replete with literary devices,
Clever, funny, erudite.
So playfully are the Gods rejected;
Much mocking wit without the spite.

Ovid's work of perverse passion
Made Augustus so very cross.
He exiled Ovid to Black Sea Tomis
And what Tomis gained was Rome's loss.'

'Oh Mr Minevar, I feel a tear welling up. In my left eye. It's always my left eye. Can you see it… welling up?'

'Aye laddie, there is a wee drop of moisture. It's very sad. One can picture poor, broken, banished Ovid walking alone along the Black Sea shore. Tomis was a barren backwater. No culture. No life. Nothing – so unlike Rome; his home. Here laddie use my hanky.'

'Thank you, Mr Minevar. You're not crying Mr M.'

'No laddie, I'm too dry to cry.'

'Another pint Mr Minevar?'

'Aye laddie, I thank ye. I'm cursed with thirst. Better make it two…'

WILLIAM RUSSELL

WHAT'S IN A NAME?

'What's next Mr Minevar?'

'It's about names. In particular, it is about the names chosen for my dear son William, known to friends and family as Will. It was Eliot who said the naming of cats is a difficult matter. The same can be said about babies. One has to be wise in one's choice. I knew a lass once, surname of Kerr, who named her son Joe.'

At least it wasn't Wayne, I mused.

'Now laddie, the poem is self-explanatory. Here it is:

'What's in a Name?: William James Isaac Russell

His name is "William Russell"
But sandwiched in-between
Are "James" and "Isaac": noble names
Which fuel his self-esteem.

For "James" is such a regal name
Of course that's clearly true
"The Wisest Fool in Christendom"
Ruled Scotland; England too.

Now "Isaac" sounds so exotic
Brimful of pedigree
And "James" is also biblical
Full of history all agree.

There's "James Joyce", the Irish voice
From Scotland came "James Watt".
America bore "Prof. James Watson"
Such an intellectual lot.

There's "James Cook" the Yorkshireman,
A mariner supreme.
"James Martin" the master chef,
Every gourmet's dream.

I chose "Isaac" for its antiquity,
Also its claim to fame.
From the scientist, the genius
"Isaac Newton" was his name.

Yes, they say he was a genius
The champion of his Age
That tour de force *Principia*
Was written by the sage.

A Cambridge man, Professor too
So intelligent was he
With high IQ, the clever chap
Encoded gravity.

But let us turn to "William",
The first name of the four.
It has its roots in "La Belle France"
"Guillaume" in days of yore.

"William" is so historical,
The famous fill the pages
Of Science, Art and Literature;
All feature down the ages.

There's "William Shakespeare", "William Blake",
The poet "Wordsworth" too,
The politician "William Pitt",
The designer "William Pugh".

"William Caxton", "William Tell"
And "William Hague" the Tory.
Let's not forget, "Holman Hunt",
Whose paintings tell a story.'

'Oh Mr Minevar, you exhaust me! But did you not think
of his contracted name of "Will"?'

'No, I did not. However, I can tell from the tone of your
voice you wish me to improvise. Very well. I shall improvise.'

And this is what he said:

'But what about the name of "Will"?
You cry with anguished voice.
Fear not, I say in my reply
Just listen to my choice.

We can of course salute "Will Self"
The writer of great books.
All hail! The actor called "Will Smith"
Renowned for his good looks.

Now laddie I'm going to fast forward to the end of the poem. Will caught me in the act of composition, thus the poem ended with him as the poetic voice:

Oh no, not more poems!
Any more and I'll get triggered
Though when I come to think of it
My name's more than I figured.

So thank you Dad for what you've done
And for all the folks you named.
You never know, if you cross my palm
I might even have it framed.

'Triggered", by the way, means to be upset,' he added.

'I hope you don't mind me saying Mr Minevar, but it feels a trifle unpolished.'

'I do mind laddie. The point is, I was interrupted... like Coleridge.'

And I laughed at his pretension.

'I'll tell you what laddie, my tongue is stuck to the roof of my mouth. It's hot, is it not?'

'Another pint, Mr Minevar?'

'You're very kind.'

IMOGEN RUSSELL

THE LOST MINNOW & THE LOST RING

'My next poem,' said Mr Minevar, 'concerns my lovely daughter Imogen. She was in Bristol with friends, got drunk, swam in Bristol harbour and lost a valuable ring. As you know, she's shortened her name to Imo. It's all in the poem. Mere scribble.'

Mr Minevar cleared his throat, proclaiming the poem's title:

'The Lost Minnow and the Lost Ring

I've nothing against the Great White Shark,
The Thresher or the Mako
But I prefer a smaller fish
In short, the little Minnow.

The reason is without a doubt
As clear as mountain water.
This little fish, so full of life
Reminds me of my daughter.

Both sprites are they, so full of vim,
Always on the go.
A sheer delight to be with them
As *fish*anadoes know!

And something else connects the two
Something that's quite profound;
'Tis a moral tale about a ring
That once was lost, was found.

Aged 20 and a lively lass
She enjoys a drink or two
And swims in Bristol harbour
Such a silly thing to do.'

Mr Minevar stopped for a moment to take a sip of beer. Then continued:

'Once drunk she *dived* into the harbour
'Twas such a foolish thing
And when safe on land, she cried out loud:
"I think I've lost my ring!"'

Mr Minevar applied the brakes again.

'It is here that Imo makes a wish. If parents are reading this to their young children, they can ask them to do the same. Anyway,' said Mr Minevar, 'I'll continue:

And yes, you've guessed it, clever clogs
It was found by Mr Minnow

Who, with fin outstretched and with a smile
Presented it to Imo.

"Oh thank you Sir", she cried with glee
"I confess I have been naughty
But Mr Minnow don't you find
This water is quite salty?

'Cos normally you are found
Elsewhere in fresh water
And surely you must agree with me
That's something that you oughter…'"

And here Mr Minevar feigned a stern voice:

"'…know Mr Minnow.'"

Mr Minevar seemed pleased with his rendition of a cross
Imo. Then continued:

'Mr Minnow had a curious voice
'Twas something like a cockney.
"Gawd 'elp me Miss, 'cos I am lost
And all me friends will mock me.

Gawd 'elp me Miss, I'm all at sea
Is there somefing I can 'ave?"
"Of course there is", Imo replied
"Take this, my own satnav.

It's waterproof and pressure proof
Oh, this button you must press.
Solar-powered, eco-green
It works by GPS."

"Oh fank you Miss, you've saved me life
You've made me pleased as Punch
I'll be 'ome for tea, or better still
I might be 'ome for lunch.'"

Mr Minevar stopped to wet his palette. Then resumed:

'And I'm glad to report that Minnow
Returned to home and glory
But is this just a fishy tale
A "souped-up" kind of story?

Of how a precious ring was found
By a fish called Mr Minnow
Delivered by this first-class male
To my belovèd Imo.'

'Oh, I like that, Mr Minevar, conflating male chivalry and virtue with the postal service.'

'Quite,' said Mr Minevar, but winter seemed to have seasoned his face. 'On with the poem,' and there was a certain brittleness to his voice that soon softened:

'Well, Imo, yes I made it up
It took me quite a while

It is a token of my love
I hope it made you smile.

Yes, Imo it's a piscine story
That ends on a happy note
A ring retrieved, a girl relieved
A poem: the best that I have wrote.'

'But the moral, Mr Minevar. The moral?'
But there was no reply. Just a flash of annoyance.
Then ten tense seconds later he said:

'And the moral of this story is:
If in despair you make a wish
No knight in shining armour comes
Instead, there comes a fish!'

'There's a touch of "Alice" in that poem Mr M.'
'Look laddie. Can a fish survive without water?'
'Meaning?'
'I'm a wee bit parched.'
'Another pint Mr Minevar?'
'You're very kind.'

EARTHWORMS

COMPOST-MAKING & HOME-BREWING

'My next poem is also close to my heart. You may have noticed that I enjoy a tipple?'

'Indeed I have, Mr Minevar. As my wallet is my witness, indeed I have.'

'Well laddie, if I were to write a poem that incorporated love, worms and beer, would you think it odd?'

'Indeed I would, Mr Minevar. Very odd.'

'And to give a poem two titles – also odd?'

'Yes, very odd.'

'All will become clear laddie. All will become clear. And here are the titles:

1. The Herculean Effort of George Edward Minevar to seduce and entice his lovely wife to his World of Worms by paying heartfelt homage to that much undervalued subterranean creature; the worm <u>Ersenia foetida</u>.

   Also, Master Brewer.

2. The Dilemma of Emma: To stay or to go.

Emma love, do come and see
My pride, my joy, my wormery.

Oh look! There they are, like bits of string
Each a muscly wriggly thing
Which end is which, you'll soon find out
When one end turns into a "snout".

My worms are Brandling, Tiger and Red.
Beetroot and turnips keep them well fed.
Different worm names for one kind of beast;
Add onions and lettuce to make them a feast.

Emma love, observe and see
The workings of my wormery

'Tis Alchemy in all but name
'Cos what goes in is not the same
As what comes out, the exit hole
Is just like paste; no longer whole.

Nothing here goes to waste
Chunky food-bits turned to paste
Rapacious is their quest for food
The transformation rather crude.

As anything organic goes
Into their mouth or up their nose
A lettuce leaf, a blade of grass
At last extruded from their arse.

I say "at last" because you see
It seems to take eternity
Yes, nothing here is done in haste
They take their time to make the paste.

Emma love do come and see
How my two worms can turn to three.

See how they writhe, their bodies supple
As one joins one to become a couple
Side by side each holding tight
And each a fine hermaphrodite.

Male and female, all in one
Is evolution poking fun
At my poor worms – June/Jim
Or is it Trisha/Tiny Tim?

Emma love do come and see
The products of my wormery

Now you have two choices – dry or wet
(For me the wet's a better bet).
But first the dry; it looks like peat:
Production is a facile feat.

First, dry the paste into a powder
So fine the grain, it is just like chowder
Then apply the stuff (in truth their faeces)
To any kind of floral species.

And vegetables will grow with vigour
Tasty, better, truly bigger
Superior to your neighbour's lot
All envy you your veggie plot.'

'Mr Minevar, I like it, but now can you shine a light on
the home-brewing part of the poem?'
'All right laddie, I'll tap into it, just as you wish.

Emma, please please don't go. Stay a while
I've something else that will make you smile.

Just look at that, my liquid brew
It needs a name; that much is true
Not silly names like Bruce or Roger
But rude and rustic like "Old Todger".

Yes, "Old Todger" is the best there is
In slang they say "it does the biz"
It is, of course, a homemade brew
All thanks to me and me trusty crew.

The "take home" message is very clear
"Old Todger" is by far the best
The crème de la crème; it has no peer;
Puts into the shade, all the rest.

Emma, come back I haven't finished
There's plenty more to be said.
"No George, no – I'm bored, tired and sleepy
It's nearly midnight; I'm off to bed."'

'Crikey Mr Minevar. Attempted seduction, worm poo and beer. All in one!'

'Indeed that is so; 'tis a very secular Trinity.'

'Do you garden Mr Minevar?'

"If you have a garden and library, you have everything you need" – Cicero Laddie. Cicero.'

Mr Minevar switched tack. 'Do you know what "Hope" is laddie? You need to look further than Pliny the Elder. "Hope is the pillar that holds up the world. Hope is the dream of a waking man."'

He paused – just for a moment.

'One can picture the hope of the man who, languishing in the desert, with parched tongue, blistered lips and sunken eyes sees a shimmering oasis. Or is it a mirage? No moisture: no life.'

'Another drink Mr Minevar?'

'You're very kind.'

DARWIN

'Now Darwin,' said Mr Minevar, 'was a genius. And they are a rare breed. His work encompasses all manner of living organisms. Much ridiculed, he was helped through the media-trashing by his friends. High on the list was Darwin's Bulldog, Thomas Huxley. His bite was equal to his bark.'

'I have heard the name.'

'A talented family; Thomas, Julian, Aldous, Andrew, and by marriage, Elspeth – wonderful writer. But first a wee word or two about Darwin and earthworms. He was keen to know if earthworms could hear.'

'What did he do?'

'His initial ploy was to shout at them. Very loudly. Screamed at the top of his voice.'

'Any joy?'

'Nothing laddie. Futile. Just made himself hoarse. Plan B was to get his eldest son to entertain them with his bassoon.'

'Odd. Any luck?'

'No. Not a single wriggle. They remained resolutely down in their earthy bunkers. Then, to Darwin's delight, they detected vibrations – when placed on top of a piano being played. Yes, Darwin knew a lot about earthworms. Barnacles too. And,' said Mr Minevar, 'he penned a marvellous book: _The Formation of Vegetable Mould through the Action of Worms, with Observation of their Habits._ Clever chap, Darwin. Anyway, here's my homage to Darwin:

> Chimp, Gorilla, Orangutan
> Genetically relate to Man
> The close match to our DNA
> Supports what Darwin had to say
>
> In Victorian England it was much debated
> How Man and Ape could be related
> Rallying friends dispensed with glee
> That fossil, the church, the enemy.
>
> As Bishop Sam overpraised our species
> Huxley's reply blew him to pieces.
>
> Yes, Darwin spawned a revolution
> Explaining much of evolution
> How evolution had direction
> The process was "Natural Selection".
>
> An act of genius that he saw
> Though Nature's red in tooth and claw
> That whilst some offspring sadly died
> If others lived, the species thrived.'

I felt the urge to speak. 'Mr Minevar...'
'George, for Christ's sake, call me George.'

'Well George, I believe I'm right in saying, that Darwin said "It is not the strongest of the species that survives, nor the most intelligent that survives. It is the one that is most adaptable to change."'

'I think I can trump that,' said Mr Minevar. 'Darwin was full of insight. Hear this: "we stopped looking for monsters under our bed when we realised they were inside us."'

'Gosh, how very modern. And I think he also said, "Animals whom we have made our slaves we do not consider to be our equal."'

'Indeed yes. I can see that the Darwinian quotation table says it's 2:1 to you. May I continue with my poem? You must try not to interrupt.'

'So sorry, yes I will try. Very hard.' But I was fizzing to ask a question. Yes, fizzing.

'Adaptation was the key
Unlocking Nature's mystery
Emasculating God's holy plan
Where Eve and Adam begat Man.'

With excess fizz on board, I just had to interrupt. I defizzed. 'Do you believe in God, George?'

'No. Absolutely not. No.' And a little puff of smoke exited from his left ear, courtesy of a perforated left eardrum. The Rubicon had been crossed. Then I looked at a second smoke signal which could only mean the man was extremely miffed.

'I've nearly finished it. Do not, I repeat, not, interrupt me again.'

He continued:

21

'Religious faith was cut to pieces
By Darwin's book _Origin of Species_.

I thought that it was not the time to tell him that he had rhymed "pieces" with "species" twice during the course of the poem. After all, the man still looked a trifle miffed. Then after a long stare, he said, 'There, J'ai finis.'

'Are you thirsty George?'

'Drier than the Gobi Desert.'

I trod the path I knew so well.

CHURCHILL

ALCOHOL

'There are lots of quotes relating to alcohol,' said Mr Minevar. 'I'll mention a few for ye, but first one of my own.

> "To err is human, to forgive divine"
> Forget all that, let's drink some wine.
> Eight bottles of this, we will soon be smashed
> And all my poems will be Ogden Nash'd.

A wee bit unfair on Ogden and although he did like a drink or two, it was only early in his career.'

A pause…

'Actually,' said Mr Minevar, 'I rather like his poetry. Terse, witty, unique.'

Another pause… I filled the gap. 'Was it not Henry Youngman who quipped "When I read about the evils of drink, I gave up reading"?'

'Indeed it was.'

'And was it not Dr Samuel Johnson who wrote, "This is one of the disadvantages of wine, it makes a man mistake words for thoughts"?'

'Indeed it was. And in a very similar vein, it was Swift who wrote there is "an old saying and a true, much drinking, little thinking". Of course, Churchill would have refuted this. Witness his oft quoted praise of alcohol, "I have taken more out of alcohol than alcohol has taken out of me". And on that note laddie, have a sip of Churchill at war.

> Some say that excess alcohol
> Causes cognitive decline
> Brandy, beer, gin and vodka
> Cider, whisky, port or wine.
>
> But as Churchill said the benefit
> Of drink outweighed the negative
> In World War II, it was for him
> Both a tonic and a sedative.
>
> A drink for breakfast and for lunch
> In the afternoon a snooze
> The evening meal fit for a King
> Much fortified by booze.
>
> His favourite drink, as we all know
> Was brandy with champagne.
> More potent than almost any drug
> It helped to keep him sane.
>
> The magic mix aided him
> To make great stirring speeches
> And when the tide of war was turned
> We arrived on Norman beaches

And thus it can be justly claimed
The war was partly won
By imbibing of fermented juice
As well as by the gun.'

'Mr Minevar, you do seem to be well acquainted with the Devil's brew.'

There was no immediate comment. A nerve had been touched.

Finally, he said: 'Many a man and woman has been bewitched by alcohol. It was Dr Thomas Fuller who wrote that "Bacchus hath drowned more men than Neptune". Well laddie, I will confess the next poem was written about my taste for the sauce. It was written by that snake in the grass, Richard Arbuthnot.'

Mr Minevar composed himself.

'Here's what that bastard Arbuthnot has to say about my marriage to alcohol.' And it was with a solemn voice he read the verse of that venomous viper, Dr Richard Arbuthnot, The Bastard.

ALCOHOL & MR MINEVAR by Dr Richard Arbuthnot

They say that Mr Minevar
Can drain the fullest minibar
Gin and Tonic, Rum and Coke
He can outdrink almost any bloke.

Six pints of ale, five of lager
Unabated goes the drinking saga
Till red of eyes and foggy head
One neurone says it's time for bed.

And in the morning, 'tis no surprise
He rises slowly, decrusts his eyes
No time to shave; just time to think
"Of course, I'll have another drink."

And so each day's a Groundhog Day
Of emptied glasses, muddled thinking
A body starting to decay
And all because of excess drinking.

Pickled liver, blotchy skin,
Bloated tummy, clueless grin,
Dishevelled hair, unshaven face,
Jaundiced eyes, no saving grace…

Beware of Bacchus that false God
Who leads you down the path to death.
Yes, ending up with your destruction
Shrunken, shrivelled, with no breath.'

'Blimey, blimey, that was a bit heavy, Mr Minevar. Nasty
Dr Arbuthnot. Are you thirsty Mr Minevar?'
'No, I'm fine at the moment.'

LOOKING AT A PAINTING

A moment later Mr Minevar was again exercising his vocal cords. 'Churchill was pretty good with the paint and easel. And a dab hand at bricklaying.'

'Yes, Mr Minevar, I know.'

There was a small lull in the conversation. It's odd how the brain functions.

I kicked off first.

'Do you ever think of death, Mr Minevar? It seems to shadow me. Even my dreams are troubled – like that chap painted by Goya. All those demons pouring out of his head.'

'I know what you mean laddie. No one can escape the scythe. Think of it as sleep laddie. Just a big sleep.'

We both had a moment of introspection.

'Homo bulla est' said Mr Minevar, breaking the silence.

'I don't follow, Mr Minevar.'

'Man is a bubble. Fragile – could go pop at any moment. Vanitas. I believe the first work of art in that genre was Jacques de Gheyn II's _Vanitas Still Life (1603)_ – skull beneath a soap bubble, laddie. I wrote a poem about Vanitas,' said Mr Minevar. 'It was brief, mind you. Bit like life really.

Looking at a Painting

"I'll be with you in a moment
I'm just looking at this painting."
Withered Tulips. A broken egg.
It's Dutch.
I know that much.
Quite easy on the eye,
I note the skull and butterfly.
And, of course, the hourglass
Empty. Vanitas.

Carpe Diem: Seize the day.
Carpe Diem: That's what I say.
"Yes. OK. I'm coming."

'Are you thirsty, Mr Minevar?'
'Give me Lake Superior, the mighty Amazon, and Victoria Falls. All three could not quench my thirst.'
'Well have a pint, Mr M.'
'You're very kind.'

EDWARD LEAR

Drinks over. Play resumed.

'Have you heard of Edward Lear?' asked Mr Minevar.

'Indeed I have – _The Owl and the Pussy Cat_ and…'

'Just so. Well, I penned a few lines about Edward. Mere scribble. I think I can remember. It is very simple; unlike Mr Lear.'

And this is what I heard:

> 'Edward Lear was such a dear
> Who wrote such melodic verse
> His literary trick, the limerick
> Is so easy to rehearse.
>
> Yes, Edward Lear wrote nonsense verse
> That's where his genius lay.
> Also, his drawings of pen and ink
> Were well thought of in his day.
>
> Let's mention first, his harmonious verse
> That some of you will know

E.g. *The Owl and the Pussy Cat*
And *The Yonghy-Bonghy-Bo*.

I'm rather fond, though it's rather sad,
Of *The Pobble Who Has No Toes*.
On an even sadder note, he also wrote
Of *The Dong with the Luminous Nose*.

I felt the urge to speak. It was Ying and Yang again. Ying said "Speak". Yang said "No". Ying won.

'George,' (and I congratulated myself for calling him by his first name) 'I understand that Lear suffered from epilepsy and he was, how can I put it, a repressed Victorian. An inveterate traveller, proficient with paint on canvas, but repressed. Unlucky in love. And melancholic to boot.'

'Yes, to all you've just said. I shall *now* continue. Do *not*, I repeat, do *not* give me any more jaw jaw. At least not until I've finished:

Often beneath the levity
One can sense a different mood.
There's a love that's unrequited
That leads to solitude.

Now Mr Lear could also paint
Abroad or whilst at home
Birds, landscapes, cities too
Like the majesty of Rome.

Yes, Italy was the country
That he liked the best

And at San Remo, I'll let you know
Poor Lear was laid to rest.

So R.I.P Mr Lear
You wrote Nonsense Verse sublime.
Your delightful verse, without a doubt
Remembered for all time.'

'Mr Minevar, are you thirsty?'

'Drier than a thrice baked Dorset Knob biscuit. And believe me that's dry. Delicious, but dry.'

'Same again?'

'You're very kind.'

THE FLIDGE

'Do you like Nonsense Verse?' asked Mr Minevar.

'Indeed I do, Mr Minevar. Indeed I do.'

'I had a bash at it once,' said Mr Minevar. Then with a trace of a smile, asked me a curious question – 'Have you ever seen a Flidge?'

'No never.'

'Neither have I, but they do exist and here's how:

When Mrs Flea met Mr Midge
They reproduced and produced a Flidge
It could neither leap, nor fly
"Oh poor young thing!" I hear you cry

Now as you know:

A flea can jump to Olympian heights
They specialise in "Fleasby Flops"
Whilst Midges dart around and hover
Flidges locomote by hops.

Their mouthparts defy all description
Their feeding habits rather crude

Inheriting parental genes
'Tis mainly blood that is their food.

Their vision is always 20:20
This the same for day and night
Never sleeping, always active
Though usually passive, they sometimes fight.

Communication is no problem
In fact, they socialise quite well.
No talk allowed, their lips are sealed
They all communicate by smell.'

'Like ants,' I enthused. 'You know, chemicals... er, pheromones. That's what ants do. They pick up the scent with their antennae which whirl and wave around like crazy. Black ants, red ants, wood ants, they all do it.'

'Have you quite finished?' said an annoyed Mr Minevar, and truth be told, I could detect a whiff of Minevarian pheromone. A bit acidic, I thought. And Mr Minevar gave me the stare of the Medusa, before continuing:

'If annoyed they will emit a gas
That matches their emotional state
When angry the gas is very toxic
Produced at an alarming rate.

But when in courtship, oh all is different
Sweet perfume pervades the air,
Not toxic, but intoxicating
As Flidge plus one becomes a pair.

So if you see a strange new insect
Slightly resembling flea and midge
It is in fact a brand new species;
That rarity that is a Flidge.'

'Oh Mr Minevar, Mr M, that's lovely,' and I clapped my hands together, gave myself a little hug and said, 'How can I put it... just lovely.' A full five seconds later, I spoke again... 'lovely.'

'Are you thirsty Mr Minevar?' He spoke just four words. 'Dry. Very, very dry.'

And I toddled off to the bar. The Master had spoken.

LOVE

'Were you ever in love Mr Minevar? I mean deeply Mills
and Boony in love. Would the heat of your passion melt the
hardest of Cheddars?'

'Indeed I was laddie – thee is a wee bit personal, but yes.
As Socrates said, "One word frees us from all the weight and
pains of life. That word is love". But there is also separation
and divorce. Real pain laddie.'

And he seemed to be wrestling with his emotions.

'Do you think you will marry again, Mr Minevar?'

'As Dr Samuel Johnson said, "A second marriage is the
triumph of hope over experience". No laddie, I'll be driving
in the single lane from now on. But hey, let's raise and clink
our glasses to love.' And we did.

> 'Feel the heat of my desire
> Enough to melt Antarctic ice
> I bid that you would be my wife
> To make my life like paradise.

> When you're not here, how dark my thoughts,
> How wan the sun that shackles life.

How frozen are my unkissed lips;
Unfreeze them now, please be my wife.

No Artist's brush could paint your blush
Divinely delicate is its hue.
Breath on breath I see your soul
Within your eyes of azure blue.'

'Sorry Mr Minevar, I mean George. Its not your best is it? A bit sickly, don't you think?'

'Yes lad. But wait until you hear the ending. You'll be asking for a bucket. I'll give you the ending; then the bucket.

Bid that you were spring and I were summer
How bright and sunny life would be.
No winter tempest to blight our future.
Our life of sweetest harmony.

Right, there's your bucket.'

'Are you thirsty, Mr Minevar?'
'As dry as the wit of Swift.'
'Me too, I'll get some drinks.'

SEPARATION

& MARRIAGE

'Now we get to the painful part,' said Mr Minevar. 'Separation. Divorce. When true love flounders, you feel very, very flat.'

'Like the fish,' I quipped.

But Mr Minevar just sighed, 'I'll say no more. Just take a look at the poem.' And I did. It was called _Separation_:

Daedalus and

Icarus equipped with wings, took flight.

Very near the sun, flew Icarus

Oblivious of his height

"Remember," had said Daedalus, "take heed of my advice."

"Come down you fool!" cried Daedalus, not once, or twice, but thrice

Examination of the body showed poor Icarus had drowned.

Daedalus knew that on this day, King Hubris had been crowned.

'Hubris, Mr Minevar?'

'Yes, Hubris laddie. It played a large role in Greek mythology. The Gods did not take kindly to Mankind overreaching itself – applied to both men and women. Punishment ensued.'

'Bit depressing that, Mr Minevar.'

'Yes lad.'

'Do you find writing cathartic?'

'Aye lad, I do. I wrote another poem. About my "melted marriage" – mere scribble.

> How sad that it should end like this
> For both of us, bereft of bliss
> Forgetting all our marriage vows
> So soon the marriage plagued with rows
>
> I did not know what I know now
> Your ring of gold was just a token
> The marriage ring you gave to me
> As hollow words were spoken.'

'Stop George! Please this is *too* much. *Too* much.
There was a pause of pain.

'Are you thirsty Mr Minevar?'

'I'm as dry as a witch's tit.'

'I'll take that as a yes.'

EPILOGUE

But by now the shadows were lengthening and a cool breeze had started to stir the leaves on some nearby trees. Beech, Oak and Birch. I wondered whether Mr Minevar had penned any pastoral poems and wanted to ask him whether he had read much of Blake, Keats or Coleridge. I thought better of it, believing we had both spoken enough. But Mr Minevar thought otherwise.

'Will ye be writing any poems yourself laddie?'

'Yes, I've one in mind.'

'What is it called?'

Beneath a Copper Sky. It's a love poem. It was summer and I was in a small boat with my dad. The sea was calm. And we talked: Man and Boy. And above us was this beautiful copper sky. It was magical... I just haven't quite found the words to write it.'

We both fell silent.

It was Mr Minevar who spoke first. 'Well laddie, we've come a long way. It's like the King in _Alice in Wonderland_ says, "Begin at the beginning and go on till you come to the end: then stop".'

'Yes, it's been an unusual day Mr Minevar. Interesting and eclectic. I've enjoyed your company Mr Minevar, I mean George. Thank you; I hope we can meet again.'

'Thank ye laddie. The same to ye. Oh, just one thing laddie. I'll be travelling home by Shanks's pony. On foot that is. No driving, you understand.'

'I see, George, so just one for the road is it?'

'You're so very kind.'

'One or a half?'

'I've got this wretched thirst laddie. Better make it two.'

ACKNOWLEDGEMENTS

I should like to thank Troubador for all their help with the production of this book. Their support and guidance were invaluable; special thanks to Fern Bushnell, Production Manager. Many thanks to Danni Durick who did the typing and last but certainly not least a heart felt thanks to my son Will who helped me with my computer and to Imo my daughter who drew the cover picture of Mr Minevar. Any errors remaining are entirely my own .

The poem regarding compost-making and home-brewing was the result of my friendship with Dr Richard Baxter and his lovely wife Emma.